This book was given to

___Hudson___

by: ___Bo___

on: ___July 27, 2013___
(date)

published by Penny Laine Papers, Inc. and printed on acid free paper for optimal archival qualities

www.pennylainepapers.com

Printed in China

WOW

...I'm a Big Brother!

Written by Penny Nye
Illustrated by Kathryn Vingi Gage

penny laine papers.

DALLAS   KNOXVILLE

WOW

...I'm a Big Brother!

(attach photo or draw a picture)

My name is

_____

and I live in

_____

(city and state)

on

_____

(name of street)

I am _____ years old and these are 3 things I think
a BIG BROTHER should do . . .

1. _____
_____
_____

2. _____
_____
_____

3. _____
_____
_____

My

baby brother / baby sister

(circle one)

is named _____ .

He / She

was born on _____

at _____.

Where was I when

_____

(baby's name)

was born?

I was with _____

at _____ .

I think the baby looks just like

_____!

(attach photo or draw a picture)

(attach photo or draw a picture)

The first time MOMMY let ME hold

_____

(baby's name)

we were at _____ .

MY FAMILY!

(attach photo or draw a picture)

I think the best thing about

belonging to my family is. . .

_____

_____

_____

_____

_____ .

Some of the special things that I do with
my MOMMY are

_____

_____

_____

_____

_____

_____!

Some of the special things that I do with
my DADDY are

_____

_____

_____

_____

_____

_____ !

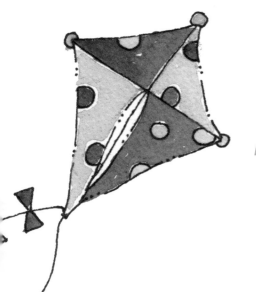

My little brother/sister
(circle one)

needs to learn to

_____

_____

_____

_____

_____ .

It's my job to teach

_____
(baby's name)

how to_____

_____

_____

_____

_____ .

MY first word was ...

I think that the BABY'S
first word will be....

Mommy and Daddy think I am an
AWESOME
big brother!

(attach photo or draw a picture)

I think that being a

BIG BROTHER

is important because . . .

I can't wait for _____
(baby's name)

to be _____ years old so we can _____

_____

_____

_____

_____ !

PhOtOs...etc...

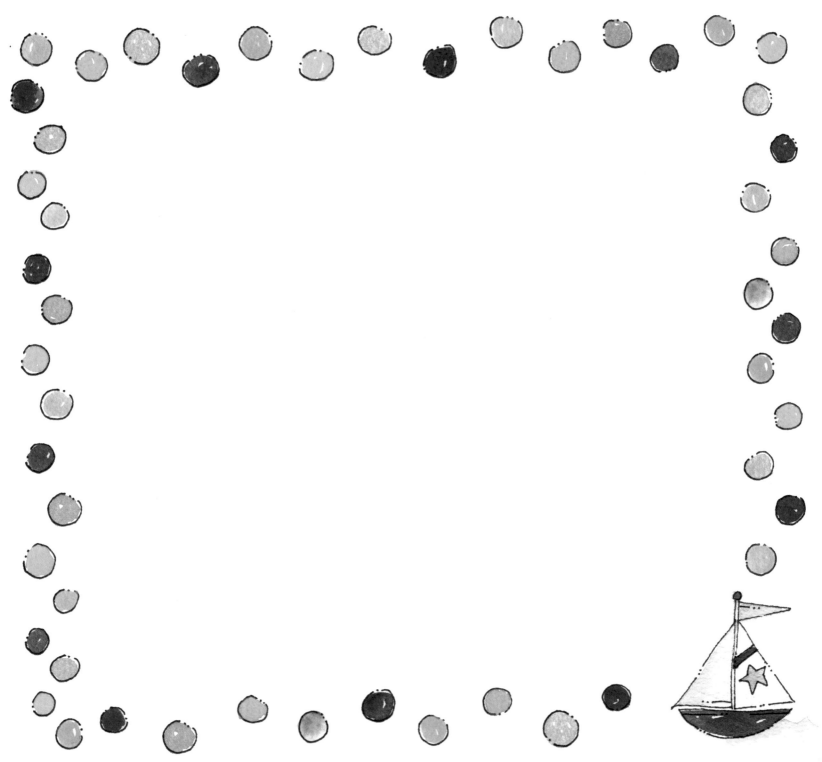

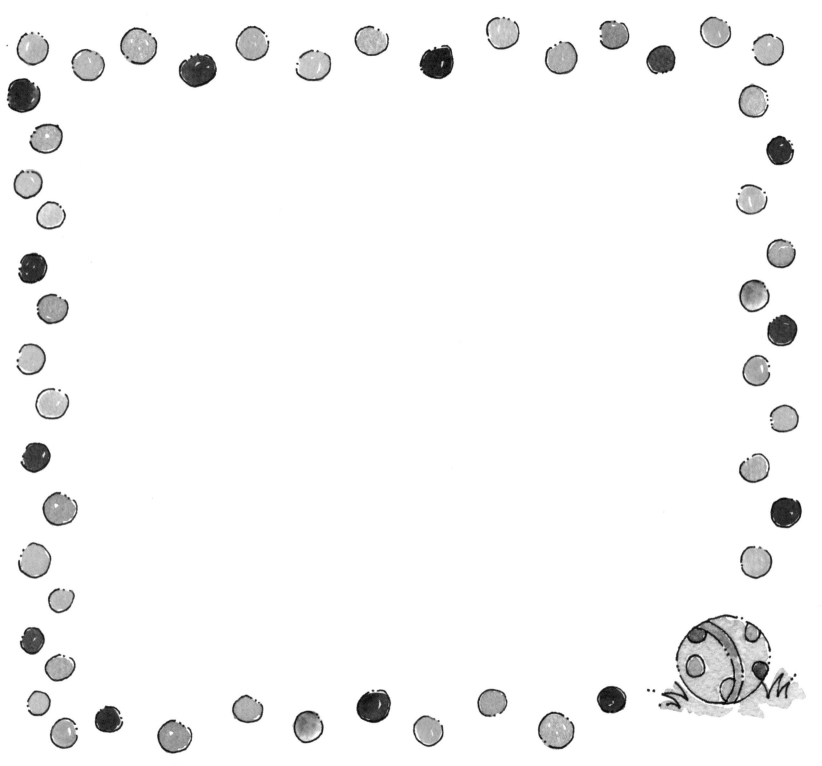

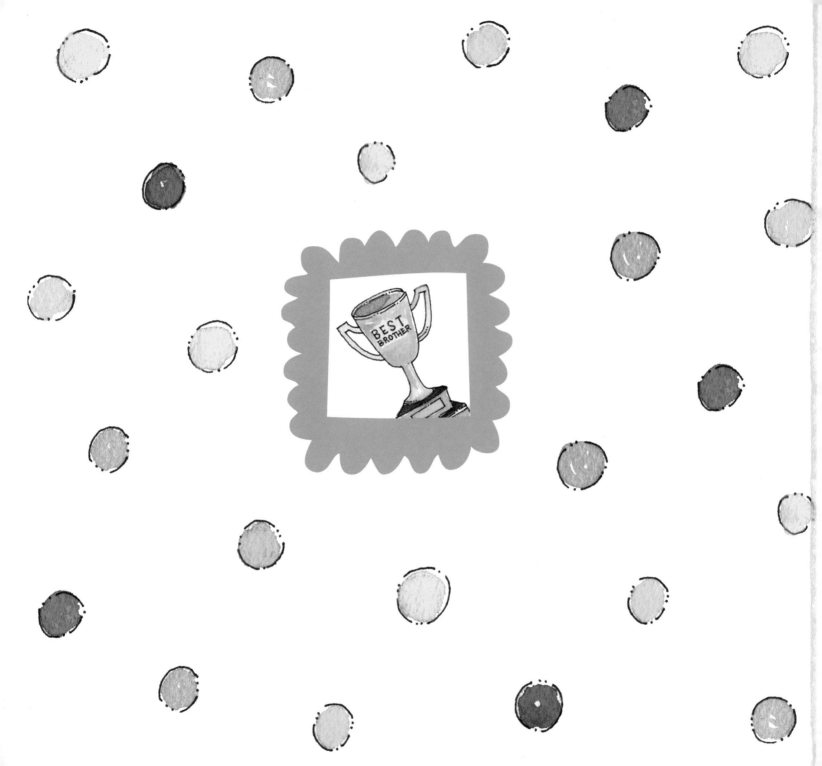